Problem Solving Activities
with
UNIFIX Cubes

By Janine Blinko and Noel Graham

Illustrated by Mike Spoor

Published by Didax Educational Resources
in association with
Claire Publications

Copyright © 1993
Noel Graham and Janine Blinko

First published 1993

Published by
Didax Educational Resources
in association with Claire Publications
395 Main Street
Rowley, MA 01969

ISBN 1 871098 18 1

Printed in Great Britain

Introduction

There are many ways to learn mathematics. One of the most successful with elementary school pupils is to involve them in problem-solving activities that are meaningful to them and can be solved with a familiar and flexible piece of equipment.

In our work with children we have found UNIFIX Cubes to be the ideal medium to enable us to develop children's confidence, knowledge, skills and enjoyment in mathematics. The activities in this book have been developed over a number of years with elementary school pupils of varying ages and abilities. They are designed for children working alone or in groups with a minimum of teacher support. Each activity begins with something that virtually all pupils can immerse themselves in. The activity is then extended and is almost always followed by a "bet you can't" activity to challenge them.

In the teacher notes we give the age of the children we have found use the ideas most successfully together with the mathematics covered. We hope that teachers and pupils will take the work on into other areas of mathematics as well as other parts of the curriculum, particularly English and science.

These are intentionally not "quiet" activities. Pupils will need to talk, guess, make mistakes and even have a few laughs. They should be encouraged to do so. There are no right answers for many of the activities. Each child or group of children should develop their own and be able to discuss their findings with others. Some teachers have found that many of the activities can be done at home for children and parents to do together who have either borrowed or bought their own Unifix Cubes. The overall goal is to have pupils work and think mathematically in an environment that is supporting, purposeful and most of all enjoyable.

Objectives and Age Levels

Guess how many spaces.
Place cubes on them and count.

Put them so you can count
them easily.

1. Give each of your friends one cube.
   Do you have enough?
2. Find something to hold the cubes.
3. Make a tower with the cubes.
   Now find two things taller than the
   tower.

Bet you can't
*Make two rectangles
with the cubes.*

Use four colors to make Suki Snail.
Use the same number of each color.

1. How many of each color did you use?

2. Make another snail the same size.
   Only use red, blue and green to make it.

3. How many of each did you use?

Bet you can't
Change your snail.
Make $\frac{1}{4}$ yellow, $\frac{1}{4}$ black,
$\frac{1}{4}$ white and $\frac{1}{4}$ blue.
Use six cubes of each color.

Make two rods.
Make one rod three
cubes longer
than the other.

How many cubes are in each rod?

1. Make two more rods with a
   difference of three.
   How many cubes in each rod?

2. Make two more rods with a
   difference of three.
   How many cubes in each rod?

3. Put all your rods in order of size.

Bet you can't
*Make five rods with a
difference of four and put
them in order of size.*

Take 19 cubes.
Place them in this order.

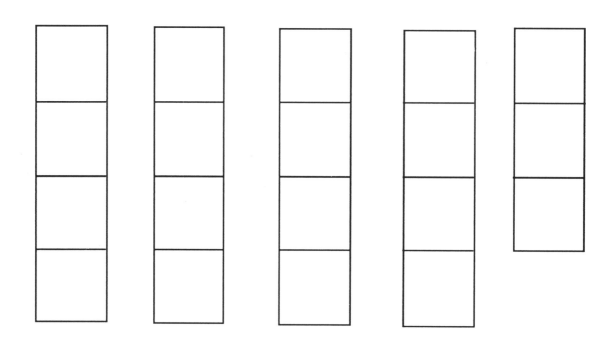

Find two new ways to group them.
Which way is easiest to count?

1. Can you group the cubes in three's?

2. Arrange your cubes like this;
   5 + 5 + 5 + 4 = 19

3. Make ten different arrangements totaling 19.

Bet you can't
Arrange cubes to show this number sentence (5 x 4) - 1 = 19

Use red, orange, white and brown
cubes.
Make as many different pairs as you can.
Are there enough spaces?

How many different pairs did you make?

1. How can you be sure you have all
   the different pairs?

2. How many different sets of three cubes can you
   make with red, orange, white and brown?

3. Choose four friends.
   Tell them to shake hands with each other.
   Everyone must shake hands with everyone.
   How many handshakes?

Bet you can't
Invent a "four" problem of your own.

Use this price list. Place the right color cubes on the spaces.

Red	1¢
Yellow	2¢
Green	3¢
Light Blue	4¢
Orange	5¢
Dark Blue	6¢
Brown	7¢
Black	8¢
White	9¢
Maroon	10¢

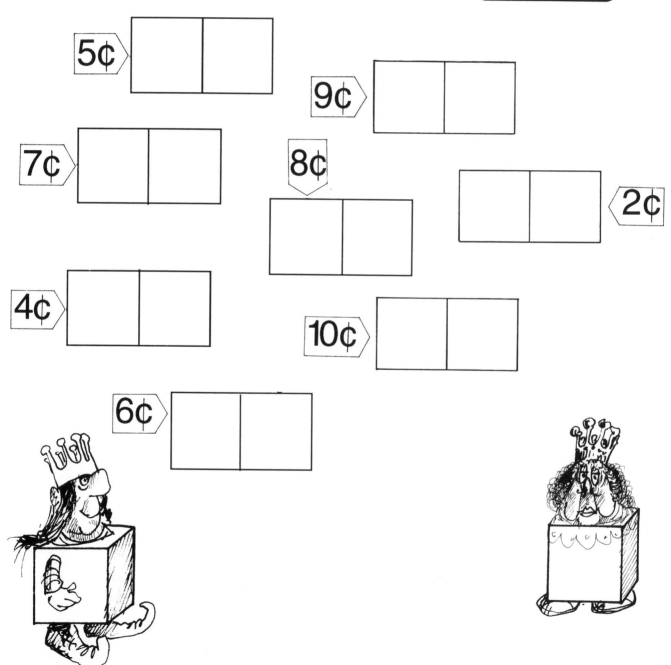

1. Use orange cubes.
   Make a model worth 50 cents.

2. Use green and orange cubes.
   Make five models worth less than
   18 cents each.

3. Use two colors of cubes.
   Make five models worth 17 cents each.

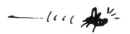

Bet you can't
*Make a model which uses all ten
colors and is worth more than $1.00.*

Guess how many spaces are
on the page.
Put a cube on
each space.

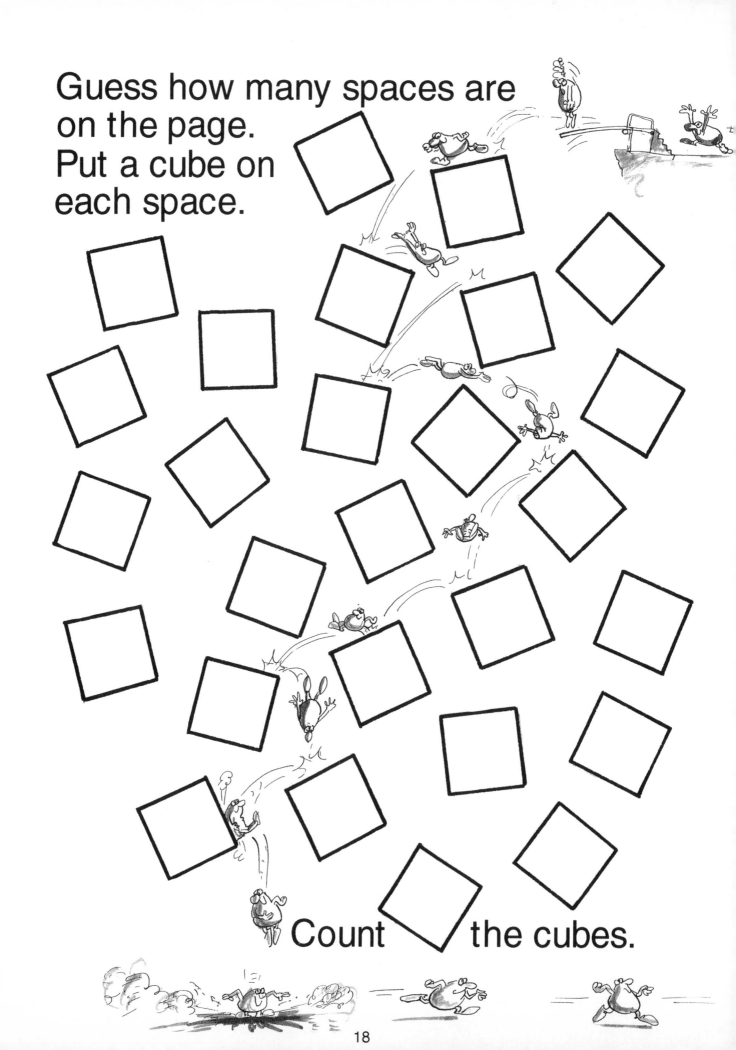

Count the cubes.

1. Make a big cube with them.

2. Can you put them into three equal groups?

3. Can you group them so that only two groups are the same size?

Bet you can't
Make three groups.
There must be a difference of
one between them all.

Use ten cubes to make a tower.

Is it as tall as you are?

1. Guess how many more you will need to make a tower which comes up to your waist.
   Try it. Were you right?

2. Guess how many more you will need to make a tower which comes up to your shoulder.
   Try it. Were you right?

3. Guess how many more cubes you will need to make a tower as tall as you.
   Try it. Were you right?

Bet you can't
Make a tower as tall as your teacher.

Ask your friends to take their favorite color cube.
Which color is the most popular.

Build a graph with the cubes.

1. Which color rod is the longest?
2. Now ask each child in the class to pick his or her favorite color.
3. Is the same color rod still the longest?

Bet you can't
Guess the favorite color of another class. Find out if you are right.

How many cubes will fit around
the edge of this leaf?
Guess. Then count the cubes.

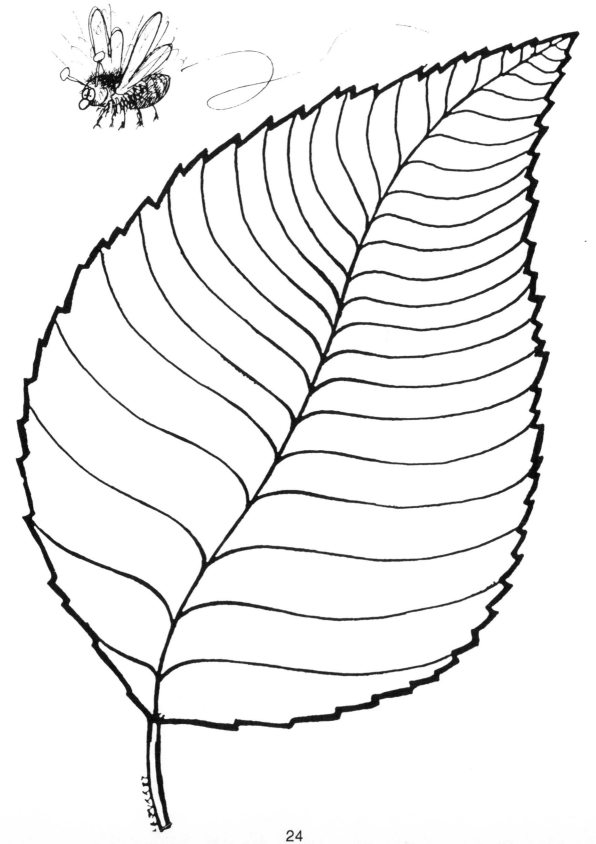

1. Use the same cubes to make a rod.
   Is it as long as your arm?

2. Do you think that all of the cubes
   in your rod will fit into the leaf?
   Guess, then count.

3. Do twice as many fit into the leaf?

Bet you can't
*Lie on the ground.
Ask a friend to draw around you with chalk.
Find out how many cubes are needed to go
around the outline.*

How many cubes will fit on the leaf? Guess the number of cubes you will need. Cover the leaf with cubes. Count them.

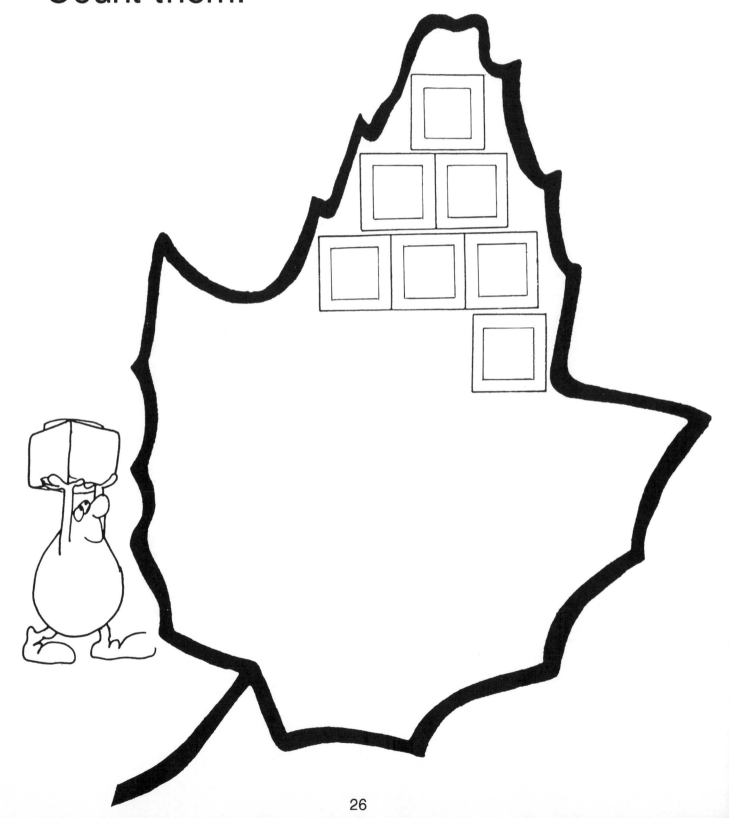

1. Ask a friend to put cubes on the leaf. Did you get the same number?

2. Draw another leaf which will hold the same number of cubes.

Bet you can't
Outline your foot. Guess how many cubes will cover your footprint.
See if you were right.

Guess how many cubes will cover this footprint.

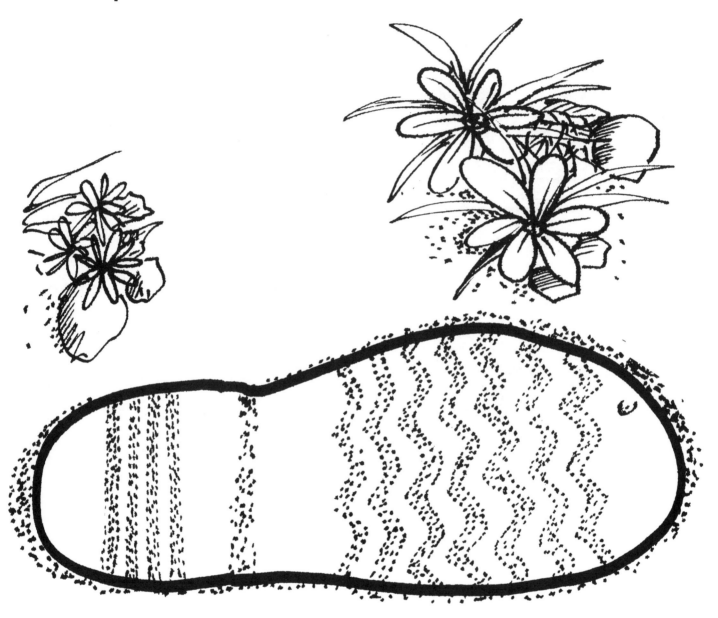

Guess how many will go around it.
Were you right?

This footprint is half the size of the first.

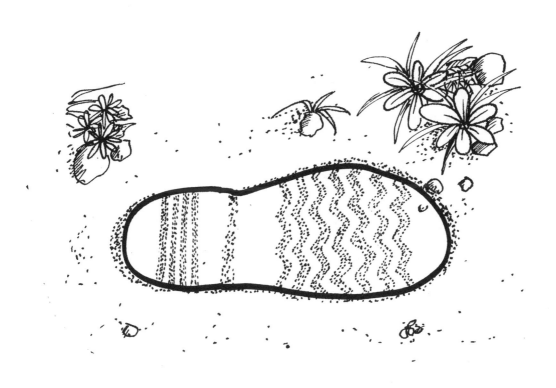

1. Guess how many cubes you will need to cover this footprint.

2. Guess how many cubes you will need to go around the edge of this footprint.

3. Were your guesses correct?

Bet you can't
Draw a footprint two times the size of your footprint.

Make a 0 - 100 number line.

0   20   40   60   80   100

Guess how many cubes will go around your teacher's foot.

Ask six friends to estimate.

Put an 'x' by everyone's guess on the number line.

Try it.
Who was closest?

Make a chart like this to show the results.

Guessed too many	Guessed just right	Guessed too few
Diane		

Try again tomorrow with someone else's foot.

Find five empty boxes.
Fill them all with cubes.

1. Count the cubes in each box.
   Write the number on the box.

2. Which box holds the most cubes?

3. Which box holds the fewest cubes?

Bet you can't
*Put the boxes in order,
largest to smallest.*

Take ten cubes.

Find three things lighter than ten cubes.

1. Find three things heavier than ten cubes.

2. Find one thing which balances with ten cubes exactly.

3. Find two things which together balance with the ten cubes.

Bet you can't
Find three things which together balance with 20 cubes.

Make a 0 - 100 number line.

```
0        20        40        60        80       100
|         |         |         |         |         |
```

Guess how many cubes will balance
with your shoe.
Mark the number on the number line.

Try it.
What is the difference between your
guess and the number of cubes you
used?

Find something different to guess and balance every day for a week.

Do you get better at guessing?

Bet you can't
Change the game into a guessing game for measuring length.

Use four red and four blue cubes to finish this pattern.

red	blue	red	blue				

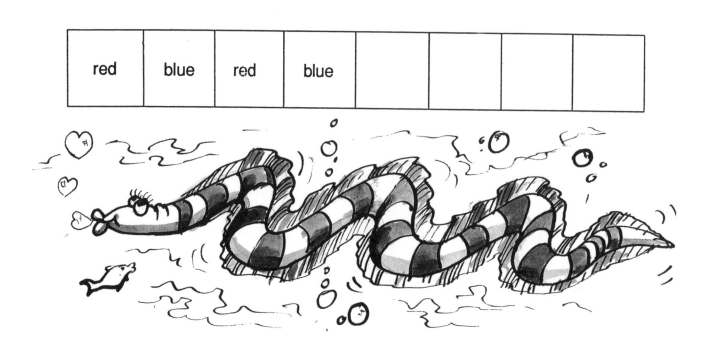

Using the four red and four blue cubes, make a different pattern.

1. Use four red and four blue cubes
   to make three more patterns.

2. Use four red, four blue and four yellow
   cubes to make four different patterns.

3. Use eight red and eight blue cubes to
   make a really interesting pattern.

Place rods of red, black and green
cubes on these spaces.
Make a symmetrical pattern.

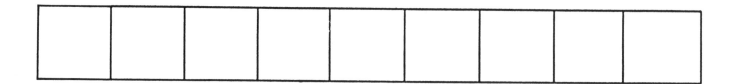

Add more cubes to make your pattern symmetrical in both directions.

Bet you can't
Extend your pattern to fit a grid like this.

Use black and white cubes to make rods. Put the rods of cubes on the spaces. Make a pattern which grows.

Make the same pattern in two directions.

Bet you can't
Extend the pattern to make a 9 x 9 grid pattern.

Use 11 cubes.
Make a pattern on the squares.

Can you make a different pattern?

1. Use 11 cubes.
   How many different patterns can you make?

2. Use 15 cubes.
   How many different patterns can you make now?

3. Add an extra space.
   Now how many patterns can you make
   with 15 cubes?

Bet you can't
*Use 28 cubes and make
a pattern that grows.*

Use 17 cubes on these spaces.

Make 10 different patterns.

1. Use 17 cubes on nine spaces.
   Can you make a symmetrical pattern?

2. Use 17 cubes on five spaces.
   Can you make a symmetrical pattern?

3. Use 17 cubes on eight spaces.
   Can you make a symmetrical pattern?

Bet you can't
*Fit 17 cubes on other numbers of spaces.
Which ones can you make symmetrical
patterns on? Why?*

Use red, yellow and blue cubes.
Make as many pairs as you can.
How many different pairs did you make?

Are there too many spaces?

1. Now use green, black and red cubes.
   Can you make more pairs?

2. Think of three friends.
   Choose two of them, then choose two different ones.
   How many different ways can you choose two of your three friends?

3. Choose three flavors of ice cream.
   How many different double-decker ice-cream cones can you make?

Bet you can't
Figure out how many triple-decker ice-cream cones you could make with three flavors.

You need blue cubes for yourself, and red cubes for a friend.

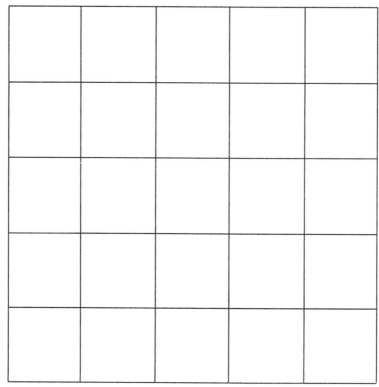

Take turns placing cubes on the grid. The winner is the first player to have four cubes in a line.

1. Can you find a way to always win?

2. Can you find a way to always lose?

Bet you can't
Change the game so it can be played in three dimensions.

Which cubes?

1. Put five yellow cubes and five black cubes in a bag.
   (Don't let anyone see what you do!)

2. Tell a friend that there are ten cubes in the bag.

3. Ask your friend to take out two cubes and put them back.

4. Ask him or her to have three more turns at taking two cubes
   out and putting them back.

5. Let your friend guess how many yellow and how many
   black cubes there are in the bag.

   Was your friend right?

Change the game:

1. Try using different numbers of yellow and black cubes.
2. Take turns in filling the bag with cubes.
3. Have five turns each.
4. Keep score and see who is the best guesser.

Bet you can't
Figure out what the chances are of choosing one black and one yellow cube when there are five black and five yellow cubes in the bag.

Take a handful of cubes.
Make rods with cubes which are
the same color.

Rods of more than two cubes	Rods of not more than two cubes

Sort the rods on this chart.

1. Sort the rods in a different way.
   Record your results.

2. Take more cubes and rods, add
   them to your rods.

3. Find a way to sort them into three piles.

Bet you can't
Find three different ways to sort 50 cubes.
Which is the best way?

Cube Town

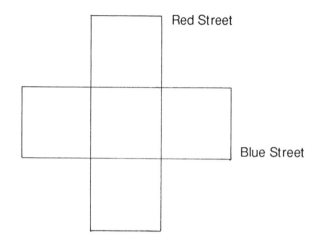

Red Street

Blue Street

Use these cubes for buildings.

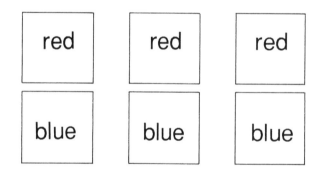

| red | red | red |
| blue | blue | blue |

Place them in Cube Town.
Where will the tallest building be?

1. Two people live in each red building
   and three people live in each blue building.
   How many people live in Cube Town?

2. Five more people move into Cube town.
   Add the correct buildings for them.

3. Make a red and blue town for 18 people.

Bet you can't
*Make a town where
50 people live.*

Yellow and Green Town

Green Street

Yellow Street

Use these cubes for buildings.

| yellow | yellow | yellow |

| green | green | green |

Place them in Yellow and Green Town. Where will the tallest building be?

1. One person lives in each yellow building and two people live in each green building. How many people live in the Yellow and Green Town?

2. Two more people move to the town. Change the town to make a home for them.

3. Use the same cubes. Make a different town. Draw it.

Bet you can't
Make a town with ten cubes which has two tall buildings.

Blue, Green and Red Town

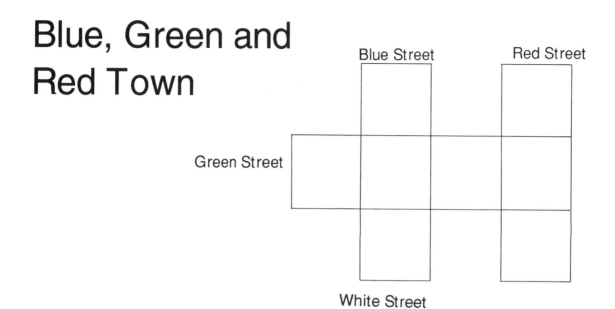

Blue Street   Red Street

Green Street

White Street

Use these cubes for buildings.

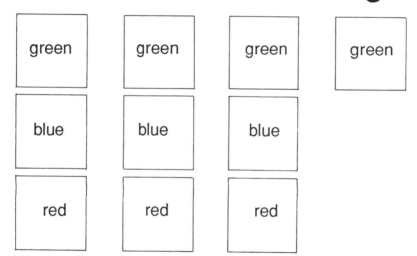

green	green	green	green
blue	blue	blue	
red	red	red	

Place them in Red, Blue and Green Town.
Where will the tall buildings be?

60

1. Red buildings cost 1¢.
   Blue buildings cost 2¢.
   Green buildings cost 3¢.
   How much does each tall building cost?

2. How much does the Blue, Green and Red Town cost?

3. Use the same cubes and make a different town
   with one tall building.

Bet you can't
*Make a town worth 50¢ using as many blue,
red and green cubes as you need.*

Cube Town

Black Street

Red Street

You need seven red, seven white and seven black cubes.
Put them on their streets.

1. Where is the tallest building?
2. If red cubes cost 1¢, white cubes cost 2¢ and black cubes cost 3¢, how much is the town worth?

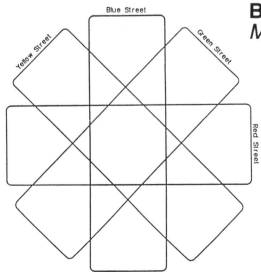

Blue Street

Yellow Street

Green Street

Red Street

Bet you can't
Make a city like this one.